SUSIE Q'S KIDS POSITIV...

My Special Angel

MW00876966

Written by
Dr. Mary Welsh

Illustrated by
Gabby Correia

PARENTS
Learn more about the
Power of Positivity.

Teach your children to lead positive and
purposeful lives following
the Four Aspects of Positive Reflection

REMEMBER -
understand your past and
cherish your memories

REFLECT -
look at how your past and
present impact your life

RECREATE -
create a 'new you', a 'new normal' in your
situation and look for the power of positivity

RELATE -
embrace your 'new you' in all that you
do, help and support others, and
give back
in our community

We started Susie Q's Kids,
a 501c3 non-profit,
to brighten and inspire the
lives of children and young adults
with our comfort bags distributed
to other nonprofits for kids in
hospitals, shelters,
foster care, grieving, and others.

To learn more, visit:

susieqskids.org
drmary@susieqskids.org

Dr. Mary Welsh
drmarywelsh.com

Read her adult grief book:
Journey into the looking Glass:
Finding Hope After the Loss of Loved Ones

This book belongs to

_____

SUSIE Q'S KIDS POSITIVE REFLECTION
My Special Angel

Susie "Q"
McBride-Welsh

Published by Author Academy Elite
PO Box 43, Powell, OH 43035
www.AuthorAcademyElite.com

Identifiers:
LCCN: 2020908195
ISBN: 978-1-64746-254-3 (paperback)
ISBN: 978-1-64746-255-0 (hardback)
ISBN: 978-1-64746-256-7 (ebook)

Available in paperback, hardback, e-book, and audiobook.

Written by Dr. Mary Welsh
Illustrated by Gabby Correia

Susie McBride-Welsh

This book is dedicated to Aunt Susie,
a special Angel and one Terrific Aunt.

We Love You!

Who are we?

Brandon

Luke

Jakob

Ella

Clara

Talk with me.
I am always with you.

Angel susie Q

Where did you go?

We miss you!

In the clouds

sparkling with the stars

By the sun and the moon

You are never alone.
I am always with you.

Just look for my
signs and talk to me.

At the beach

Around the house

In your dreams

In the garden

Look for me everywhere

Do you miss us?

Continue to color and draw.
Put your pictures on the refrigerator
so we both can see them.

Wear your hair ribbons and jewelry:
necklaces, bracelets, and pins.
Hug your teddy bear.
They have great memories we shared.

Go Lions!
Wear your team jersey and t-shirts to
the game. Play soccer, basketball,
baseball, and football.
I will always be your cheerleader
cheering for you and the team!

Remember our happy times

I have Hershey and
Abby with me.

Be kind to your pets, enjoy them
as they bring so much love, joy, and fun.
Take care of Roman and Jack.

Wear your favorite
t-shirts and hoodies.

I love 'Detroit Hustles Harder' and all
my music concert t-shirt collection.
Wear yours proudly,
they are so cool!

Do you know how we feel?

When I am hurt or sad becaus
I fell off my bike?

I am helping you up.

When I am learning new words,
I love to read!

I am listening.

When I am happy, runnin
and playing with my dogs o
my friends Brodie and AJ

I am watching and laughing

7

Always, I love you!

When I am excited, like when I am
driving my new car.

I will keep watch over the road
and keep you safe.

I did it!
When I am successful graduating
and deciding where to go to college
and decide my career.

I am your biggest cheerleader.

Congratulations!

Music is fun

"You are my sunshine"

Nana and Papa sing this song because it reminds them of you. Always happy and smiling.

"Baby shark"

Clara laughs when singing this song.

"Wheels on the bus"

Ella remembers singing this song with you, it makes her smile.

I love music.

Let's enjoy it together.

"Ten little monkeys jumping on the bed"

Luke remembers jumping on the bed and singing this song with you, it makes him laugh.

Rock on!

Awesome concerts.

We remember the fun times with you and will always think of you when we go to concerts and on tours.

Are you lonely?

Let's go to the zoo.

Let's enjoy a day at the park.

Let's go to the movies and
eat some popcorn.

No, I am always with you!

Let's visit places
we loved to go to
and visit new places.

We have a blast at Nana and Papa's swimming pool,
it is one of our favorite memories spending
the day together.

will you forget me?

Draw pictures of me.

Draw pictures of us together.

Color pictures of the garden,
the rainbow, and the sun,
moon, and stars.
Put photos in a book.

Try crafting and scrapbooking.

Continue making things with
your sewing machine.

Play the games we liked.

Basketball-put your hands up
Soccer-use your feet
Baseball-hit hard and far
Football-run fast and catch the ball

Have fun!

RECREATE

Never, Never, Never

I could never forget you, I am a part of you!

Be best friends for life!

Go to the movies, the arcade, swimming in the pool, play with the younger ones, and take me on your adventures.

I am ready to explore the world with you!

can you hear me?

I am humming along with you.

You are my sunshine,
my only sunshine

I love listening to the stories as
you read your books.

They are so exciting.

Yes. Talk to me.
I am always
listening.

Your dreams are full of fun
and great ideas.

I want to travel
with you on your adventures.

I see your good deeds,
how you watch the other kids,
and help mom and dad.

Your actions speak to me
loud and clear.

Good Job!

How can I connect with you?

Look for dandelions and blow the fuzz off.

Don't forget to make a wish.
Look for pennies.

Pennies are a good sign that someone is thinking of you.

Don't forget to make a wish.
Plant seeds and flowers.
Watch them grow.

I love beautiful flowers.
I am always in the garden.

watch for signs. There is beauty all around you.

Help in the garden.

Make special stepping stones, plant flowers, and weed and water the grass and garden.

Add a special plaque or statue.

Make it your special place to talk to me.

Cemeteries are another place to talk to loved ones.

18

Are you sad you are not with us?

Laugh
more than you cry.

You and your
emotions matter.

Talk about me.

Tell me stories of us and
your new adventures.

Look at pictures and
smile remembering us.

Listen to the music, sing,
dance, and have fun.

Be happy.
We are always
together.

I love you and you
love me too!

Make crafts like
we did together.

Bake cookies and cakes,
so yummy.

Wear that special t-shirt.
Wrap up in that special blanket.
Keep that teddy bear close.

Be yourselves,
I am so proud of you all.

20

I am lonely, I miss you.
I love you,
please support each other.

Sisters
are a best friend for life.

Be nice to her,
she loves you and will
always be there for you.

Your pets can bring you
happiness and comfort.

They are your
cuddle buddies.

Brothers are cool.

They can be your
best friends for life,
take care of each other.

Aunts and uncles are special.

Mom, dad, and the boys.

Mom, dad, and the girls.

Nana and Papa.

You have many who love you, including me!

Do you know you made me feel special?

You are the best.

Get on my level.

You are amazing.

You are my sunshine.

Yes, because you are!

You got this.

Thumbs up.

You are very special.

Keep helping others.

24

How can I help others?

Help your family,
clean your room.

Help your friend,
help him when he falls
off of his bike.

Help your neighbor,
walk their dogs and yours.

Help your teacher,
clean up and be good.

Be kind and helpful, be your best.

Help a charity,
help those that need
some assistance.

Our family created a charity called
Susie Q's Kids.

They brighten and inspire the
lives of kids to be their best.

They give comfort bags to kids
in hospitals, shelters, foster care, and
those that are grieving
so they know someone cares.

Ask your parents what
you can do to help others.

Donate a copy of this book for
another kid to read.

Be kind,
Give your time to help
make someone else smile
and feel special.

Meet my angel friends.

Hershey and Abby

sam

Grampa Tom

Grampa Art

Tania and
Joseph Gregory

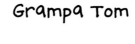

Keith

We are lucky to have friends and angels.

Who is special in your life?

Draw their pictures here.

You got this!

You are
awesome!

Be
your best!

You
are amazing!

You are
my sunshine!

Sending
good wishes
to you.

Love Susie "Q"

Made in the USA
Monee, IL
08 April 2021